We dare the author to answer the question ...

Have you ever been scared on a roller coaster?

Yes, I always feel a bit scared on roller coasters. Once I went on a ride called "The Wall of Death". You had to stand in a cage and hold on tight. Then the ride spun round fast and tilted you high up in the air. It made you feel as if you might fall out of the cage at any time. It was really scary ... but lots of fun!

For Isabelle and William

Dan and Lee were at Black Sands theme park. They were on a roller coaster called Doom Ride. Lee and Dan were in the front of a car. Mark, a kid from their school, was in the back. It was a brilliant ride.

But then it slowed down, and stopped with a jolt. Their car was stuck at the top of a hill.

"Look," said Dan. "The Doom Ride crew is coming up to get us out."

Lee pulled out the coin they had found in the woods. He tossed it up in the air. Would it say **dare** or **danger**? It hummed loudly and landed on its edge between the seats.

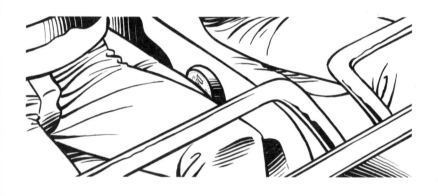

"It hasn't landed on either side this time!" he said.

The ride crew started letting people off at the back of the train. A man from the ride crew got to their car. He undid the three boys' safety harnesses.

"Sit still and don't move," said the man. "We'll help you off in a second."

But just then the ride started to move again. Their car shot forward over the hill. Lee and Dan grabbed the side of the car. They could fall out at any second. They were high up and going very fast.

"Hold tight!" yelled Lee. "This is dangerous!"

Then Dan and Lee heard Mark scream behind them. They looked back. Mark was in a panic. He was not holding on to the side of the car.

"Mark's in danger," yelled Lee. "We must help him. I'll hold on to you, Dan. You try and reach him."

Dan twisted round and reached out to Mark. "Grab my hand, Mark!" Dan shouted.

"I can't!" yelled Mark. "I'm scared."

"Just do it!" shouted Lee.

Mark grabbed Dan's hand. The cars went faster and faster.

"I can't hold on much longer," shouted Dan.

At last the ride slowed down. In a few seconds, the cars were back at the start again. Everyone cheered as the boys were helped out of the car.

"The coin was right all along," said Lee.

"What do you mean?" asked Dan.

"It landed on its edge, so it showed **danger** and **dare**," said Lee. "It was daring and dangerous to help Mark."

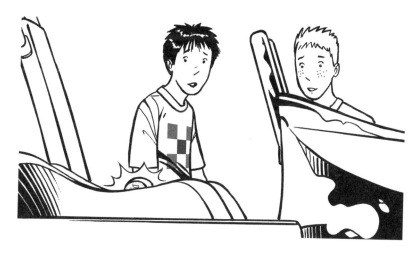

Dan looked upset. "Let's not mess around with that coin again," he said. "It's giving me the creeps."

"OK," said Lee. He put the coin in his pocket ... then he grinned. "But I bet we try it again one day!"

(This story is based on a real accident at a theme park in Holland in 2007. No one was hurt!)

Have you read all of Dan and Lee's adventures?

Raft Rescue

The coin shows Danger.

Can Dan and Lee rescue the boy from the river?

Ghost!

The coin shows Dare.

Will Dan and Lee go into the old house – and what will they find inside?

For more info check out our website:
www.barringtonstoke.co.uk

The Cliff

The coin shows Danger.

Lee slips and falls off the cliff.
Can Dan save him?

Dare You?

The coin shows Dare.

The school bully gives Lee and Dan a dare. Who will end up the loser?

Up in Flames

The coin shows Danger.

A house is on fire. A dog is trapped. Can Dan and Lee help?

For more info check out our website:
www.barringtonstoke.co.uk